CONTENTS

NOT FOR THE PUBLIC TO KNOW
TOP SECRET
ZONE 13 FILES ONLY

No
Chance

DAVID
ORME

Ransom

No Chance
by David Orme

Illustrated by Jorge Mongiovi and Ulises Carpintero
Cover photograph: © Mila Zinkova

Published by Ransom Publishing Ltd.
Radley House, 8 St. Cross Road, Winchester, Hampshire, SO23 9HX, UK
www.ransom.co.uk

ISBN   978 184167 456 8

First published in 2011
Reprinted 2013

Originally published in 1998 by Stanley Thornes Publishers Ltd.

A CIP catalogue record of this book is available from the British Library.

1

AT THE TRAFFIC LIGHTS

Julie was driving home. She had only just passed her driving test. Her mum had let her use the car to go round to Becky's house for the first time. She was driving back as carefully as possible. She didn't want to damage Mum's car. If she did, she would never be allowed to use it again.

The streets were dark. It was raining, and the windscreen wipers were working. But it was still hard to see through the windscreen.

The road was shiny with lights. Julie hadn't driven in the dark before. She was feeling nervous and wished she was already at home.

There was a red traffic light ahead. Julie slowed down and stopped. She waited for the lights to go green. It seemed to take a long time.

Just then, she saw someone standing on the pavement. It was Matt. He was one of her best friends. He had said he would meet her at Becky's house, but he hadn't turned up. Julie had been surprised, because Matt didn't usually let her down.

Matt looked pale and wet standing in the rain. Julie leant over and wound the window down.

'Matt! Why weren't you at Becky's house? What are you doing here? You look soaked! Do you want a lift?'

Matt didn't say anything. He stood and looked at Julie. He looked almost as if he was trying to work out who she was. At last, he got in. He snapped on his seatbelt. The red light changed to green and Julie drove on.

THE SILENT PASSENGER

Julie could feel Matt shivering. She took her hand off the wheel for a second and touched the skin on the back of his hand. He was freezing!

'What were you doing standing in the rain?' said Julie. 'Why didn't you come round to Becky's? We were expecting you.'

She waited for Matt to speak, but he said nothing at all. He just sat there, staring straight ahead. His shivering was getting worse. His face was whiter than any face Julie had ever seen. Rain dripped from his hair and ran down his face.

Julie was really worried now. Matt was usually such a cheerful person. He was always full of jokes. He could make anyone laugh. They had both passed their driving test on the same day and they had shared a big celebration. Matt had seemed fine then. All he could do now was sit in the car and stare straight ahead.

'What is it, Matt? Are you ill or something?'

Matt still didn't say anything. Julie decided that the best thing to do was to take him straight home. His house was quite near hers.

The rain seemed to be getting heavier and heavier. It was getting even more difficult to see the way ahead.

Julie got to the place where she had to turn off. The road went to the estate where they

both lived. She slowed down and turned the wheel – but the car went straight on!

OUT OF CONTROL

Julie couldn't control the car! She stamped on the brakes, but the car didn't slow down at all. She pulled on the gear lever, but it wouldn't move. She tried to pull out the keys, but they seemed to be stuck fast.

All this time, Matt just sat in his seat, staring out of the car. The heater was full on, but he was still shivering.

Julie looked ahead. There was a roundabout coming up. Another car was coming towards

the roundabout. Julie knew that she needed to stop and let it go first. Her car just carried on, straight on to the roundabout.

The other car had to brake hard. Would it be able to stop in time on the wet road?

It just managed to stop. It must have had good brakes and tyres. The driver pressed the horn angrily. Julie's car swung off the roundabout.

They seemed to be heading out of town. Julie was very frightened. Nothing she could do would stop the car. She turned to Matt and shook him. He just sat there, staring ahead. There was a terrible look of fear on his face.

On and on went the car. Luckily, there wasn't much traffic about at that time of night.

Julie saw a big blue sign ahead. She remembered where she was. This was the road that went to the motorway!

Julie was really frightened now. She hadn't driven on the motorway yet. It was always so busy. She didn't want to go on it in the dark. She pulled at the door handle. Maybe she could jump out of the car.

The door wasn't locked, but it wouldn't open. She tugged and tugged at the handle.

Soon she saw the signs for the motorway turning ahead. The car swung to the right. It started down the slip road. It went faster and faster.

NOT FOR THE PUBLIC TO KNOW

TOP SECRET

ZONE 13 FILES ONLY

ON THE MOTORWAY

The car shot out of the slip road straight on to the motorway. It just managed to squeeze in front of a huge truck. The driver flashed his lights and hooted. On this wet, dark night, sudden braking was dangerous; Julie's car could have caused a serious accident.

Julie looked over at Matt again. The shaking was getting worse. His face looked awful now. His eyes were staring, and his mouth had fallen open. Slowly, he lifted his hands to

cover his face. Then he screamed – a scream of terror!

Julie guessed that something terrible must have happened to Matt. Something on the motorway.

Somehow, she knew that she was about to find out what it was.

She stared through the windscreen. It was difficult to see anything. The trucks threw up spray, and the windows were steaming up. She put the windscreen wipers on faster. It didn't help much.

Then Julie saw something ahead. On the other side of the road, headlights suddenly started pointing the wrong way.

Even through the noise of the car engine, and the sound of the windscreen wipers, she could hear terrible bangs and crashes. A great, dark shape was swerving towards her out of the darkness!

A truck had crashed through the barrier. Its trailer was swinging round, straight towards Julie's car. There was no chance of avoiding it.

She put her hands over her eyes, and screamed, and screamed ...

5

WHERE IS MATT?

The crash didn't happen. Suddenly, the noise stopped. Julie took her hands from her eyes. Her car was still waiting at the traffic lights. The traffic lights where she had picked up Matt. She looked across to the pavement. There was no one there.

The lights changed to green. Shaking, Julie put the car into gear and drove on. She tried the brakes, and the car slowed down. She

moved the wheel, and the car changed direction.

She looked across to the passenger seat. It was empty. She put her hand on it. It was bone dry. Matt had been soaked. He couldn't have been in the car, yet Julie remembered touching him and feeling his cold hand.

Julie turned into the drive of her house. She sat in the car for a few minutes. She wanted to cry, but she couldn't. At last, she took off her seatbelt and got out of the car.

It had stopped raining now. She opened the front door and went in.

Her parents were standing in the hall, waiting for her. They both looked white and shocked.

Somehow, Julie knew what they were going to say.

'Julie, we've got some terrible news. We've just heard. It's Matt. He's been killed on the